language skills

Writing in Action

level f

LOYOLAPRESS.

Managing Editor	Kim Mason
Production Manager	Mary Bowers
Editors	Sandy Hazel, Jan Marcus, Margaret O'Leary
Production Staff	Phyllis Martinez, Kari Nicholls, Steve Straus
Interior Design	Mary Bowers

Acknowledgments

Grateful acknowledgment is made to the following authors, agents, and publishers for the use of copyrighted material. Every effort has been made to trace the ownership of all copyrighted material and to secure the necessary permissions to reprint these selections. Any errors or omissions are unintentional and will be corrected in future printings.

page 50: GOOD-BYE, CHICKEN LITTLE by Betsy Byars. Copyright © 1979 by Betsy Byars. Used by permission of HarperCollins Publishers.

page 88-90: SARA JANE by Sara W. Holdren. Copyright © 2002 by Sara W. Holdren. Used by permission of the author.

ISBN 0-8294-1012-0

©1997 Loyola Press
3441 N. Ashland Avenue
Chicago, Illinois 60657

All Rights Reserved.

Printed by LSC Communications,
Harrisonburg, VA
USA, March 2017, Lot 032017

WRITING BUSINESS LETTERS

What Are Business Letters?

- A sweatshirt you ordered from a catalog comes in the wrong color.
- You want to find out more about a summer camp in North Carolina.
- You want to get free tickets to the taping of a television show when you visit Los Angeles.
- You never received the free CD you sent in yogurt tops for.
- You want to get a brochure about a museum you want to visit.

What would you do if any of these things happened to you? Often, the best way to get an answer or solve a problem is to write a special kind of letter called a BUSINESS LETTER. If you know how to write a business letter that is clear, neat, and to the point, you have a better chance of getting the answer you need.

Reading a Business Letter in Block Style

Here is a business letter written by a student named Brandy March. She typed it in BLOCK STYLE. (You should type a business letter if possible. If not, use your absolute best handwriting.)

In block style, each new line begins at the left margin of the page. You do not indent, even when you begin a new paragraph. This makes it easier and faster to type business letters.

Read Brandy's letter below. Later you will fill in the numbered blanks.

1. _____

2. _____

3. _____

4. _____

5. _____

6. _____

45 Simpkin Lane
New Orleans, LA 70117
February 3, 2003

Minnesota Office of Tourism
100 Metro Square
St. Paul, MN 55101

Dear Madam or Sir:

I am writing for information on vacationing in Minnesota. My family is thinking of visiting Minnesota this summer. We want to rent a cabin on a lake, and we want to visit places where we can learn about Native American and pioneer history.

If you would please send me any free brochures you have about the best places for us to visit, I would very much appreciate it.

Very truly yours,

Brandy March

Brandy March

The Parts of a Business Letter

Let's find out more about the six parts of a business letter. As you read, look back at Brandy March's letter, identify each part, and fill in the numbered blanks with the name of the part of the letter.

1. Heading

The heading contains the writer's address, but not his or her name. Usually the heading has three lines:

- The street address of the person sending the letter
- The city, state, and ZIP Code of the address
- The date the letter is written

In some business letters, you might see a space between the last line of the address and the date. In others, you might see the date at the top of the page, followed by a space and then the writer's address. These variations are fine, but for this lesson, follow the model in Brandy's letter.

2. Inside Address

After the date in the heading, skip a line and then type the inside address. In the inside address, you give the name and address of the person or business to whom you are writing. The inside address may have three or four lines:

- The name of the person you are sending the letter to, if you know it
- The business or organization you are sending the letter to
- The street address of the business or organization
- The city, state, and ZIP Code of the address

3. Salutation

After the last line of the inside address, skip a line and then type the salutation, which is the greeting. Capitalize the name of the person you are sending the letter to, like this:

Dear Ms. Jacobs:

If you do not know the name of the person to whom you are writing, you can use one of these salutations:

Dear Sir or Madam: *or* Dear Madam or Sir:
To Whom It May Concern:

If you know the title of the person you are writing to, you can use a salutation like this:

Dear Customer Service Manager:

In a friendly letter, you end the salutation with a comma. But in a business letter, you end the salutation with a colon, like this:

Dear Dr. Levin:

4. Body

After the salutation skip a line and then type the first paragraph in the body. Remember, in block style you do not indent a new paragraph, and you skip a line between each paragraph

In a business letter, the writing in the body should be polite, brief, and to the point. This is not the time for flowery description.

As in other kinds of writing, each paragraph should have a main point. In your opening paragraph, state the reason why you are writing. In her letter, Brandy March got right to the point by saying, "I am writing for information on vacationing in Minnesota."

If you make a request in the letter, then be sure to thank the person or express your appreciation in advance. Brandy wrote, If you would please send me any free brochures you have about the best places for us to visit, I would very much appreciate it."

When you write a business letter, do not write on the back of the paper. Begin a new sheet of paper, with the number 2 at the top.

5. Closing

After the last paragraph in the body, skip a line and type the closing. Business letters use formal closings. You would not close with "Your pal" or "See you soon!" Some possible closings for a business letter are:

> Yours truly,
>
> Sincerely,
>
> Very truly yours,

Only the first letter of the closing is capitalized, and the closing ends with a comma.

6. Signature

After the closing, skip three or four lines and then type your first and last name. In the space between the closing and your typed name, sign your name in ink. The first letter of your name should line up with the first letter of the closing.

Analyze a Business Letter

Read the business letter below and answer the questions about it.

3390 Foxglove Lane
Portland, OR 97201
January 12, 2003

Customer Service Department
Super Sports Souvenirs, Inc.
1009 Mortimer St.
Atlanta, GA 30308

Dear Madam or Sir:

I hope you can help me solve a problem with a product from your company. For my birthday, I got a set of 10 baseball cards from my grandfather. They were sealed in clear plastic, with a label on the outside that said, "Inside: 10 cards!" But when I opened the plastic, there were only eight cards.

I would like to receive the two cards missing from my package. My grandfather gave me the receipt for the cards. I made a copy of the receipt and a list of the eight cards I did get. The copies are enclosed.

Thank you very much for taking care of this problem.

Sincerely,

Josh Leiberman

Josh Leiberman

1. Who wrote this letter?

_____

2. What company is the letter written to?

_____

3. Why was this letter written?

_____

_____

4. What is the heading of this letter?

_____

_____

_____

5. What is the salutation of this letter?

_____

6. What is the closing of this letter?

_____

Addressing the Envelope

Most business letters are written on paper that is 8 1/2 inches by 11 inches, and they are mailed in business envelopes that fit sheets of paper this size. When you're ready to send your letter, follow the form on the next page to address the envelope.

Your name and address

**Name and address of the
business you are writing to**

Brandy March

445 Simpkin Blvd.

New Orleans, LA 70117

Minnesota Office of Tourism

100 Metro Square

St. Paul, MN 55101

An envelope addressed for a business letter has two parts:

Your name and address

This is on the top left of the envelope, and usually consists of three lines:

- The name of the writer
- The street address of the writer
- The city, state, and ZIP Code of the writer

Name and address you are writing to

This information goes in the center in the bottom half of the envelope. It may have three or four lines, and contains:

- The name of the person at the company or organization, if you know it
- The name of the company or organization
- The street address or post office box
- The city, state, and ZIP Code of the business or organization

Pretend you are writing a letter to Marjorie Hines at the Insbruck Institute. You can write your own return address. The Insbruck Institute is at 8009 7th Avenue in Hotchkiss, NY. The ZIP Code is 10087. Address the envelope on the next page.

Writing a Request Letter

There are many times you may want to write a business letter to ask for something. For example:

- You might want to find out more about something that interests you, or request information for a report. For instance, you might write to a government agency to find out how an animal gets on the endangered list.
- You might write to a tourism bureau or a museum and ask that printed information be sent to you.
- You might write to the director of a business or community group to see if they need any volunteer help.
- You might write a letter to request tickets to a free performance or some other free offer.

Reading a Request Letter

Here is a request letter written by a student named Barry Lipinski. Notice that Barry does the following things in his letter:

- Gives brief background information to explain why he is writing
- Makes a specific request
- Ends with a courteous statement

You will also notice that Barry's letter looks a little different from the letter Brandy March wrote, which you read in the previous lesson. Brandy's letter is in block style, but Barry's letter is in semi-block style. (Semi- means "half.") This is also an acceptable way to write a business letter. In semi-block style, the heading, closing, and signature are on the right. Each paragraph in the body of the letter is indented.

21 Fairview Lane

Shelbyville, MI 48876

April 8, 2002

Manager

Jefferson Bookstore

95 Main Street

Shelbyville, MI 48876

Dear Madam or Sir:

I read in the newspaper today that one of my favorite authors, Clint Treeman, is visiting your store on May 30. I also read that there will be tickets available for a reading Mr. Treeman is giving at your store. Please put me on the list to receive two tickets.

Thank you very much for your help, and for bringing one of my favorite writers to town.

Yours truly,

Barry Lipinski

Barry Lipinski

1. What background information does Barry give?

_____

_____

_____

2. What specific request does he make?

_____

_____

3. What courteous statement does he end with?

_____

_____

Planning a Request Letter

Now it's time to practice writing a request letter. Try to think of a real request you'd like to make. If you can't, make one up.

In some ways, writing a request letter is like other kinds of writing. You follow the same steps: prewriting, drafting, revising, and proofreading. To prewrite, jot down notes for some information you might request. Here are some ideas to get you started:

- A brochure about a place you would like to visit
- Information about a musician you like or an author you admire
- Information that an expert or organization will know, such as how to volunteer to help in a zoo, or how to arrange a visit to a business that you want to know more about

Use this space to jot down notes for some requests you might make.

_____

_____

_____

Once you know what you want to request, plan what you want to say. This plan does not need to be a formal outline. To get started, answer these questions:

Background information: Why are you making this request?

_____

_____

What is your specific request?

_____

_____

You will need to find the address of the place or person you are writing. You can do this in the library or perhaps on the Internet.

Writing a Draft of a Request Letter

Type a draft of your letter in block style. Use the notes you have already written.

✓ Use the list below to make sure you include all the necessary parts of a business letter. Check off each part as you finish it.

_____ 1. The heading

_____ 2. The inside address

_____ 3. The salutation

_____ 4. The body

_____ 5. The closing

_____ 6. Your signature

Writing a Letter of Complaint

Danny Gervin bought a model car kit. When he opened it, he found that the directions were missing. He returned it to the store and exchanged it for another kit. But the directions were missing from that one as well. He tried again—still no directions!

Kimberly Cho couldn't wait to take her best friends to the Wild Kingdom amusement park for her birthday. She called ahead to make sure the park would be open. She was told, "Yes, we're open till Labor Day." But when the day came, she and her friends arrived at the park only to find the gates locked and a sign saying, "Park Closed—Please Come Back Again."

Danny and Kim have good reasons for writing a special kind of business letter called a letter of complaint.

Reading a Letter of Complaint

Read the letter of complaint on the next page. Notice that it includes:

- A clear statement of the problem, along with background information
- A suggested solution
- A courteous tone

1. Why did Jennifer Melton write this letter?

_____

_____

2. What problem does she have a complaint about ?

_____

_____

3. What solution does she ask for?

_____

_____

1229 Northview Rd.
Ithaca, NY 14850
May 18, 2002

Ilyria Marvels Company
195 Jordan Rd.
New York, NY 10010

Dear Sir or Madam:

I collect science fiction dolls, and I recently ordered a set of
Galaxy Hunter dolls from your catalog. When I received the dolls, I
liked them all very much. However, I received two Korbak dolls in the
set, but no Zorgon doll.

I would appreciate it if you would please send me the missing
Zorgon doll. If you want me to send you the duplicate Korbak doll,
please let me know.

Thank you so much for taking care of this. I know I will enjoy
the complete set!

Yours truly,

Jennifer Melton
Jennifer Melton

Tips for Writing a Complaint Letter

As you write, keep these tips in mind:

• State the problem and its background clearly and briefly. Stick to the point. Just say what happened.

• Suggest a solution. If the company can help solve your problem, explain how. If you want to keep a problem from happening again, suggest how. For example, in the case of the closed amusement park, Kimberly Cho could suggest that the people who answer the phones be alerted if the park will close.

• Be courteous. There is no need to insult or show anger in your letter. As the old saying goes, "You can catch more flies with honey than vinegar." Even though you might be upset, write in a calm and reasonable tone. The more polite and understanding you are in your letter, the more likely you are to get the result you want.

Planning a Complaint Letter

To write an effective letter of complaint, you should prewrite, draft, revise, and proofread. If you have a real complaint, go ahead and write about it. If not, think of an imaginary situation. For example:

• Being sent the wrong CD from an out-of-town company

• Being told on the phone that children's tickets were half-price at a museum and finding out that wasn't the case

• Relying on a new book for information about a hiking path and learning that the path was closed years ago

• Being told to leave a store because you were a child, even though you were well-behaved

Think of what you will write about and then plan your letter.

1. What situation or problem will you complain about?

_____

_____

_____

2. How will you ask that the situation be changed or the problem solved?

_____

_____

_____

3. What is the address of the place you are writing, and the person you are writing to? (If you are making up the complaint, then you can make up this information.)

_____

_____

_____

Writing a Draft of a Complaint Letter

Type a draft of your letter in block style. Use the notes you have already written. Remember to be courteous!

✔ Use the list below to make sure you include all the necessary parts of a business letter. Check off each part as you finish it.

_____ 1. The heading

_____ 2. The inside address

_____ 3. The salutation

_____ 4. The body

_____ 5. The closing

_____ 6. Your signature

Revising and Proofreading a Business Letter

You have written two drafts of business letters. One is a letter requesting something, and the other is a letter of complaint. Choose one of these letters to revise and proofread.

Revising Your Business Letter

A business letter that is clear, concise, and correct makes a good impression, and is more likely to get the results you want. Revising a business letter is important because you want to make sure that:

- You have all the information correct and in the proper format.
- You clearly explain the situation and what you want.
- The letter sounds courteous.

You can use the checklist below to help you revise your business letter and make sure it is as good as you can make it.

Content

_____ Does my letter clearly state why I am writing?

_____ Do I include any background necessary for the reader to understand the situation?

_____ Does each paragraph have a main point?

_____ Do I clearly ask for the specific result or action that I want?

Organization and Tone

_____ Is my letter well organized, so it is easy to follow?

_____ Is my tone businesslike—not too chatty or casual?

_____ Is my writing courteous?

Proofreading the Business Letter

You have to be extra careful when you check punctuation and spelling in a business letter. Pay special attention to all those proper names and details in the addresses. You want to make sure that all information is exactly right. If it isn't, your letter may not reach the person you want to read it. Or, if there are too many mistakes, the reader might not take your letter seriously.

☑ Check each of these items in your letter:

Correctness

_____ Are all the words spelled correctly?

_____ Are all proper names spelled correctly?

_____ Are the abbreviations correct?

_____ Do abbreviations have a period after them?

_____ Is there a comma between the day and the year in the date?

_____ Is there a comma between the town and the state in the addresses?

_____ Is there no punctuation, but only a space, between the state and the ZIP Code?

_____ Is the salutation followed by a colon?

_____ Does each sentence end with the right punctuation?

_____ Is there a comma after the closing?

_____ Are the sentences complete and not run-ons?

Format for block form:

_____ Do all lines begin at the far left margin?

_____ Is there a blank space between paragraphs?

_____ Is there space for a written signature between the closing and the printed signature?

When you are satisfied with the changes you made, make a clean copy of your letter. Address an envelope for the letter.

Folding Your Letter

There is a special way to fold a business letter. Here are the steps. Before you fold the letter you wrote, practice with another sheet of 8 1/2 by 11 inch paper.

1. Place the letter in front of you on a desk, face up.
2. Fold the bottom of the sheet up about one third. Crease the paper.
3. Fold the top of the sheet down so it is about a half-inch from the bottom crease. Now, crease the top fold.
4. Put the letter in the envelope so the top crease is at the top of the envelope. That way, when the reader opens the letter, it is facing him or her.

WRITING A COMPARE AND CONTRAST ESSAY

PREWRITING: What Is a Compare and Contrast Essay?

Imagine that you pick up a magazine, and in it you see an article that compares a popular novel about pioneers to the recent movie version of the book. The writer tells how the movie differs from the book: the movie leaves out some events and it changes the setting from Minnesota to Nebraska. The writer also tells how the book and movie are alike: the movie presents characters very faithful to the way they are described in the book. This article is a kind of COMPARE AND CONTRAST essay. It tells how two things are different from and similar to each other.

When you compare and contrast, you explain likenesses and differences. You might be asked to write a compare and contrast essay for your studies. In history, you might compare two leaders. In art, you might compare two paintings. In science, you might compare two animals. In literature, you might compare two characters.

A Reading to Compare and Contrast

You are going to read a compare and contrast essay by a student named Miguel. Miguel was assigned an essay based on a reading in History. Before you read Miguel's essay, read the article that Miguel was asked to write about.

The Spartans and the Athenians

Long ago, the ancient Greeks did not all belong to one nation. Their land was divided into many parts, called city-states. Sparta, warlike and strong, was one of the most famous city-states. An even more famous city-state was Sparta's neighbor, Athens, a place of great learning and beauty.

Sparta

The government of the Spartans reflected their warlike nature. They were ruled by two kings and a council of 28 powerful soldiers. In Sparta, men and women were taught to follow the orders given by their leaders.

The Spartans spent their whole lives preparing for war. Spartan boys and girls began training for war when they were even younger than you. When a Spartan boy was seven years old, he went to an army camp to live among the soldiers. At the camp, he was given very little clothing and very little food. If he wanted more to eat, he had to sneak out and hunt wild animals on his own. The Spartans believed that would teach the boy to look after himself. They thought soldiers who could look after themselves would be the best prepared when they went to war.

Spartan boys were taught to read, but that was all the education from books they received. On the field, every boy learned to run, jump, wrestle, fight, and hunt. They were taught not to show any feeling. If a boy cried when he was hurt, he was shamed by all the others. A boy who showed pain was not thought worthy to be a Spartan.

When a Spartan boy left for war, his mother would say, "Come back with your shield or on it." This meant, "Win, or die."

The Spartans lived hard and simple lives. They cared little for their homes and thought nothing of comfort. In Sparta, you would not find fine buildings or pretty pictures. The Spartans did not care about having or making beautiful things. Even today, we still call a person "Spartan" who lives a strict, simple life with few comforts.

Athens

In ancient Greece, the city-state of Athens was even more famous than Sparta, but it was famous for a different reason. While the Spartans prized war, honor, and glory, the Athenians loved peace, wisdom, and beauty.

In Athens, artists made beautiful paintings, statues, and buildings. In the city was a hill called the Acropolis. It was covered with beautiful temples. In these temples were beautiful statues, some made of marble, and some of ivory and gold. Many of our beautiful buildings today are copies of those ancient Athenian temples.

In government, the Athenians began a new idea that has lasted to this day. Athens is known as the birthplace of democracy. Democracy comes from Greek words meaning "the people rule." In Athens, the citizens voted to choose their leaders. Before they voted, the Athenians gathered at a special place called a forum. There, they talked about whether to vote yes or no. For example, they might vote to decide whether they should go to war.

The Athenians were the best-educated people of their time. The Athenians trained the body: the boys ran foot races, threw long spears called javelins, wrestled, and boxed. But most of all they trained the mind. An Athenian boy learned to sing and dance, to write poetry, and to speak well in public. He learned history and acting. He even learned to identify the stars in the sky.

Athens and Sparta were two very great, and very different, city-states in ancient Greece. If you lived in ancient Greece, which city-state would you want to call home?

Read a Compare and Contrast Essay

Let's look at the compare and contrast essay that Miguel wrote about Sparta and Athens. You will follow his thinking as he plans and writes his essay. Later, you'll write your own compare and contrast essay based on a reading from American history.

Miguel wrote his essay in response to this assigned topic:

Write an essay in which you compare and contrast the way people thought and behaved in Athens with the way they thought and behaved in Sparta.

When you get an assignment to write about, you need to think carefully about what the assignment is asking you to do. Look again at Miguel's assignment. Here it is with some of the key words underlined by Miguel:

Write an essay in which you <u>compare and contrast</u> the way <u>people thought and behaved in Athens</u> with the way they <u>thought and behaved in Sparta</u>.

What is the assignment asking Miguel to do? Explain in your own words:

_____

_____

To prepare to write his essay, Miguel read the information about Sparta and Athens again, and looked especially for descriptions of how they thought and behaved. He underlined the words and sentences that seemed most important to him. Then he made a list, like this:

Sparta	Athens
City-state in ancient Greece, "warlike and strong"	City-state in ancient Greece
Ruled by king and council of soldiers—followed orders	People valued art, beauty— temples, statues
Focused on preparing for war	"Birthplace of democracy"—citizens chose leaders, talked about decisions
Education—boys learned to read but mostly how to fight	Education focused on the mind, not just body
Mothers told sons, "Come back with your shield or on it."	Boys learned many things— singing, dancing, speaking
Hard lives, didn't care about beautiful things	Girls taught at home, some learned to read and write

Miguel did some more planning, but let's go ahead and look at the essay he wrote. Miguel decided to focus on ways that the Spartans and Athenians were different. Here is the final draft of his essay.

The Warlike Spartans and Artistic Athenians

Both Sparta and Athens were famous city-states in ancient Greece. Sometimes they joined together, but mostly the Spartans and Athenians thought and behaved in very different ways. While the Spartans were interested in war, the people of Athens were interested in peace. They had different kinds of government, different educations, and different ways of life.

One big difference between the Athenians and the Spartans was their government. The Spartans were taught to follow orders. The only thing they wanted was to be great soldiers, so their idea of government was to obey what their leaders said. The Athenians, however, had a very different kind of government called democracy. The citizens voted on who their leaders should be. They gathered in a forum and made big decisions together. So, for the Athenians, democracy was important, but for the Spartans, it was more important to obey orders.

The Athenians and the Spartans also had very different ideas about education. To the Spartans, education meant training to be soldiers. Boys were taught to read but they didn't spend much time with books. Instead, they spent their time learning how to wrestle, jump, fight, and be strong. While Athenians boys were taught how to keep their bodies strong, they also studied a lot more. The Athenians valued learning about many things, including music, dancing, poetry, history, and acting.. *The Athenians valued education in many ways,* but the Spartans only cared about education as a way to prepare for war.

The Spartans and the Athenians were also different in the ways they lived. The Spartans did not have comfortable homes. They did not create great art or care about having beautiful things. Instead, they lived very simple, hard lives. The people of Athens, however, cared about having beautiful things around. They had artists who made statues and paintings. They had beautiful temples, too, with marble statues. The Athenians cared about art, but the Spartans did not, because they were focused on war.

While the Spartans and Athenians were neighbors in ancient Greece, they were very different. They had different ways of governing themselves. They had different ways of educating their people. They lived in very different ways, with the Spartans living a stern life and the Athenians loving art and beauty. Both these city-states were great, but they would never be able to agree on what was important or how people should live.

Analyze a Compare and Contrast Essay

To help you understand how Miguel put together his compare and contrast essay, look at each paragraph, one at a time. Answer the following questions.

Paragraph 1: In his introduction, what does Miguel say are the similarities between Sparta and Athens? How does he say they are different?

_____

_____

Paragraph 2: What is Miguel's main point in this paragraph?

_____

_____

Paragraph 3: What is Miguel's main point in this paragraph?

_____

_____

Paragraph 4: What is Miguel's main point in this paragraph?

_____

_____

Paragraph 5: How does Miguel conclude his essay?

_____

_____

PREWRITING: Thinking About a Topic and Reading Carefully

Now you will begin to write a compare and contrast essay based on a reading about George Washington and Thomas Jefferson.

Reading for Your Compare and Contrast Essay

In your essay, you will compare and contrast two famous leaders from American history. First, read the selection below about George Washington and Thomas Jefferson.

Two Great Leaders of Our Country

We see their faces every day on the money we use. We hear them praised as great Americans. They are called two of our "founding fathers." George Washington and Thomas Jefferson shared a strong belief in American independence and in the American people. They helped turn 13 British colonies into a new nation, the United States of America.

A Gentleman Soldier

From early in his life, George Washington showed great ability as a leader and as a soldier. When George's older half-brother died, George took charge of his family's land. He also became an officer in the local army. George was young, but he easily took on the role of military leader. He quickly learned how to turn a ragged group of men into a strong force.

Washington became known for a sense of command and dignity. These qualities were to be important in the American struggle for independence from Britain. In 1775, the Continental Congress put Washington in charge of the army. The congress saw his military ability. They saw the sense of command that seemed to be part of his very bones.

The colonial troops needed a leader like Washington. They were sloppy and untrained. They did not know much about war. But Washington changed that. He brought discipline to them. He made them strong and proud. He taught them how to fight.

General Washington respected the ordinary men he led. He did not feel he was better than his soldiers. He ate the food his troops ate. He slept where they slept. His troops saw this and admired him. They followed him without question. His leadership was a key reason the rebels won the war for independence.

Washington was so loved and respected that almost everyone agreed he was the right man to become our first president. As leader of the new nation, Washington did not want to be a king. He wanted the new government to be a government of the people, not by a king.

A Man of Words and Ideas

Thomas Jefferson loved learning. From the time he was a boy, he never sat down to rest without a book. He went to college and law school, studying everything from math to philosophy.

Jefferson was not a great soldier or speaker, but he was a brilliant thinker and a gifted writer. In the American struggle for independence, he made his greatest contribution through his pen. He was given the job of writing the Declaration of Independence. Even today, the words of this document are famous all over the world.

Jefferson knew more about writing and ideas than about fighting wars. This sometimes caused problems when he served as governor of Virginia during the years of the American Revolution, because many battles were fought in Virginia. When his term as governor ended, he said the colony needed a leader with more military skill.

Jefferson went home, but he was soon needed to serve the newly born United States. He was elected to Congress. Then, in 1800, he was elected President. He served two terms. Like Washington, Jefferson did not think the United States should have a king. In fact, Jefferson wore plain clothes to show that the president should be a man of the people. This angered some foreign visitors, who thought the president was showing them no respect.

Jefferson, however, did have respect—for the people. He wrote the words that helped create a nation dedicated to the belief that "all men are created equal." His words still ring true today.

Analyzing an Assigned Topic

Here is your assigned topic for this essay:

George Washington and Thomas Jefferson were two great Americans. Use the reading to compare and contrast their abilities, their roles in the American Revolution, and their attitudes.

After you have read the topic, take some time to think carefully about what you are being asked to write.

Miguel started by underlining important words in his assigned topic. You try it. Look again at your assigned topic and underline the key words, below:

George Washington and Thomas Jefferson were two great Americans. Use the reading to compare and contrast their abilities, their roles in the American Revolution, and their attitudes.

Read and Think

When you write an essay on an assigned reading, the key to doing a good job is to pay careful attention to the reading.

Before you go farther, carefully reread the selection about Washington and Jefferson. As you read, underline or highlight important words and sentences that relate to the key terms in the assignment. The key terms include "their roles in the American Revolution," and "alike and different in their abilities and their attitudes."

For example, here is how you might underline important words in the first paragraph about George Washington:

> From early in his life, George Washington showed <u>great ability as a leader and as a soldier</u>. When George's older half-brother died, George <u>took charge</u> of his family's land. He also became an <u>officer in the local army</u>. George was young, but he easily took on the role of <u>military leader</u>. He quickly learned how to turn a ragged group of men into a strong force.

After you reread the selection about Jefferson and Washington, answer the following questions:

1. Titles and subtitles in readings can give clues to what is important in the reading. Look at the title of the reading selection and at the subtitle of each section. What do these tell you about how Washington and Jefferson were alike and different?

_____

_____

_____

_____

2. What similarities between Washington and Jefferson are shown by the introductory paragraph (which begins, "We see their faces...")?

_____

_____

_____

In the next lesson, you will plan and organize your essay. Remember, the key to writing a good essay on an assigned reading is to pay careful attention to the reading.

PREWRITING: Planning the Essay

So far you have thought about the topic, reread the selection, and written notes on your reading. Now it's time to organize your thoughts into a plan for the essay.

Organizing: Finding the Main Points to Compare and Contrast

Before Miguel wrote his essay about the Spartans and the Athenians, he planned what he would write. He knew that he needed to compare and contrast the two city-states. He also knew that he couldn't just write a long list of likenesses and differences. He needed to organize his essay so that each paragraph would focus on one main point.

Miguel looked over his notes about Sparta and Athens to help him think of main points to compare and contrast. For example, in his notes, he noticed that he wrote about education in both Sparta and Athens:

Sparta	Athens
Education— boys learned to read but mostly how to fight	Education focused on the mind, not just body Boys learned many things— singing, dancing, speaking

So, Miguel decided that in one paragraph he would focus on education in Sparta and Athens. After looking over his notes and looking back at the readings, he came up with the following points to compare and contrast:

Point to compare	Sparta	Athens
Government	ruled by king and council of soldiers—followed orders	"birthplace of democracy" —citizens chose leaders, talked about decisions
Education	education—boys learned to read but mostly how to fight	education focused on the mind, not just body; boys learned many things—singing, dancing, speaking
Way they lived	hard lives, didn't care about beautiful things	people valued art, beauty—temples, statues

Using a Chart to Plan Your Essay

Like Miguel, you will use a chart to plan your essay. What points will you compare and contrast? Sometimes the topic gives you clues about the points to compare. Look again at the topic for your essay:

George Washington and Thomas Jefferson were two great Americans. Use the reading to compare and contrast their abilities, their roles in the American Revolution, and their attitudes.

The topic is guiding you to compare and contrast three points:

    1. Their abilities

    2. Their roles in the American Revolution

    3. Their attitudes

Using a Chart to Plan Your Essay

☑ Use the chart below to plan your essay. You will need to look back to the reading for the information to put in the chart.

Point to compare	Washington	Jefferson
Abilities		
Roles in American Revolution		
Attitudes		

DRAFTING: Beginning the Draft

Now it's time to build on the work you've done and begin writing a draft of your compare and contrast essay.

As you know, essays usually have three parts:

• introduction

• body

• conclusion

Today's lesson guides you through writing the body, and leaves the introduction and conclusion for the next lesson.

Writing Focused Paragraphs in the Body

Each paragraph in the body of your essay should begin with a topic sentence. The topic sentence should announce the main point of the paragraph. The rest of the sentences in the paragraph should support the main point announced in the topic sentence. If they do, then you have written a focused paragraph.

In Miguel's essay, each paragraph follows a pattern, like this:

1. topic sentence: point to compare
2. examples about Sparta
3. examples about Athens
4. closing sentence: reinforces main point

Here is a paragraph from Miguel's essay. The sentences are numbered to show the pattern he followed.

[1] One big difference between the Athenians and the Spartans was their government. [2] The Spartans were taught to follow orders. The only thing they wanted was to be great soldiers, so their idea of government was to obey what their leaders said. [3] The Athenians, however, had a very different kind of government called democracy. The citizens voted on who their leaders

should be. They gathered in a forum and made big decisions together. [4] So, for the Athenians, democracy was important, but for the Spartans, it was more important to obey orders.

A Plan for Your Essay

You can follow a similar pattern when you write the body paragraphs of your essay. Write three body paragraphs, and for each paragraph, write the following:

First body paragraph: abilities

    topic sentence: point to compare

    examples about Washington

    examples about Jefferson

    closing sentence: reinforces main point

Second body paragraph: roles in American Revolution

    topic sentence: point to compare

    examples about Washington

    examples about Jefferson

    closing sentence: reinforces main point

Third body paragraph: attitudes

    topic sentence: point to compare

    examples about Washington

    examples about Jefferson

    closing sentence: reinforces main point

✓ On a separate sheet, write the draft of the body of your essay. Look back to the chart you filled in on page 33, or check the reading if you need more details than are in your chart. Begin each paragraph with a topic sentence. Keep each paragraph focused on the idea announced in the topic sentence.

This is not the time to worry too much about spelling, punctuation, and other details. Instead, focus on getting your ideas down as clearly as you can. Double-space to leave room for revisions later.

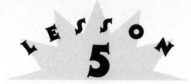

DRAFTING: Completing the Draft

Today you should finish writing the draft of your compare and contrast essay. To get your ideas fresh in your mind, begin by rereading the body paragraphs you have written so far.

Writing the Introduction

The job of the introduction in a compare and contrast essay is to:

- Identify what you will be comparing and contrasting: for example, a book and the movie based on the book, or two characters from different stories, or two great American leaders.

- Preview the main points of comparison. For example, look at Miguel's introduction below.

> Both Sparta and Athens were famous city-states in ancient Greece. Sometimes they joined together, but mostly the Spartans and Athenians thought and behaved in very different ways. While the Spartans were interested in war, the people of Athens were interested in peace. They had different kinds of government, different educations, and different ways of life.

Look again at the last sentence in Miguel's introduction: "They had different kinds of government, different educations, and different ways of life." It is Miguel's *thesis statement.*

In a compare and contrast essay, the THESIS STATEMENT announces the specific points you will compare and contrast.

It helps your reader if you announce your points in the order in which you will discuss them. Miguel's thesis statement lets his reader know that she can expect to read about education, government, and ways of life. And that's exactly what Miguel provides, in that order.

✓ On a separate sheet of paper, write a draft of your introduction. Remember to:
- Identify what you will be comparing and contrasting.
- Preview the main points.
- End with a thesis statement that announces the specific points you will compare, in the order you will compare them.

You're writing a draft, so don't worry too much about spelling, punctuation, and other details. Double-space to leave room for revisions later.

Writing the Conclusion

In a compare and contrast essay, the conclusion is your chance to summarize the similarities and differences you have written about. When you summarize, you briefly restate the main points.

In the conclusion, you can also try to end with a sentence or two that the reader will remember. Here is Miguel's conclusion:

> While the Spartans and Athenians were neighbors in ancient Greece, they were very different. They had different ways of governing themselves. They had different ways of educating their people. They lived in very different ways, with the Spartans living a stern life and the Athenians loving art and beauty. Both these city-states were great, but they would never be able to agree on what was important or how people should live.

In Miguel's conclusion, he briefly reinforces the main differences between the two city-states and ends with a sentence that brings the essay to a satisfying close: "Both these city-states were great, but they would never be able to agree on what was important or how people should live."

✓ Now, write a draft of your conclusion, including a brief summary of the main similarities and differences. Double-space to leave room for revisions later.

Linking Ideas with Transitions

Transitions are words and expressions that help readers move smoothly from paragraph to paragraph and from sentence to sentence. They show how one idea is related to another. Transitions are especially important in a compare and contrast essay.

Transitions to Show Similarities

Read this sentence, which begins Miguel's essay:

Both Sparta and Athens were famous city-states in ancient Greece.

The word *both* helps show a similarity between Sparta and Athens.

Here are some transitional words and phrases that show similarities:

just as	so too	like
similarly	likewise	neither has
both have	also has	in the same way

Transitions to Show Differences

Here are some transitional words and phrases that show differences:

however	in contrast to	although
on the other hand	but	whereas
unlike	yet	though

For example, in the following paragraph, notice how Miguel uses "however" to signal that a contrast is coming:

One big difference between the Athenians and the Spartans was their government. The Spartans were taught to follow orders. The only thing they wanted was to be great soldiers, so their idea of government was to obey what their leaders said. The Athenians, however, had a very different kind of government called democracy. The citizens voted on who their leaders should be.

☑ Now go back through your draft and see if you can make your ideas clearer by revising sentences to use transitions.

Revising and Proofreading the Compare and Contrast Essay

Now that you have a complete draft of your compare and contrast essay, it's time to revise your work to make it as good as it can be. Look at each of the following elements of the essay in turn. Revise when you see that the essay can be improved. Once you are satisfied that you've done as good a job as you can, check off the item.

Revising to Improve Content and Organization

First you look at the big picture—your ideas and how they are organized.

Introduction

_____ Does my introduction identify what I am comparing and contrasting in the essay?

_____ Does my introduction end with a thesis statement that announces the points I am comparing, in order?

Body

_____ Does each paragraph include a topic sentence?

_____ Is each paragraph focused? Do the rest of the sentences in the paragraph all support the topic sentence?

Conclusion

_____ Does the conclusion summarize the main points of comparison between the two subjects?

Proofreading for Grammar and Mechanics

Once you have revised the content and organization of your essay, it is time to proofread carefully for correctness.

Grammar

    _____ Is each sentence complete, with a subject and a verb?

    _____ Is the writing free of run-on sentences or sentence fragments?

Punctuation

    _____ Does every sentence end with the correct punctuation mark?

    _____ Are commas, apostrophes, and quotation marks used correctly?

Spelling

    _____ Are all words spelled correctly?

✓ When you have checked every item, you are finished. Make a clean, final copy of your compare and contrast essay.

WRITING A CHARACTER SKETCH

LESSON 1

PREWRITING: What Is a Character Sketch?

Why do you admire certain people? What makes others unforgettable? Who is a hero to you and why?

Think of a person who fascinates you. (Choose someone outside your family.) On the lines below, try to explain what it is about the person that you find so interesting.

_____

_____

_____

Perhaps your answers are like the ones that follow: because she is a good athlete; because he has a mind of his own; because she is talented; because he seems mysterious. Many factors determine your attitude toward people, whether you know them personally or not:

    1. Appearance—how they look

    2. Behavior—how they act

    3. Speech—how they talk

    4. Achievements—what they have accomplished

A CHARACTER SKETCH recreates a person from the writer's point of view, based upon observations of that person.

By carefully watching people and listening to what they say, you develop feelings or impressions, both good and bad, about them. In this essay, you will use words to recreate a person whom you know or have observed, just as a photographer takes a picture or an artist creates an image.

Choosing a Character

To write a captivating character sketch, you must choose a suitable character. The suggestions on this page will help you. For best results, do not choose the following people:

1. A person in your immediate family (that is, a parent, brother, or sister)

2. A person your own age (such as a fellow student)

3. A person who is younger than you (for example, someone you baby-sit)

With these suggestions in mind, whom will you choose as a subject?

You should feel that the person looks, speaks, and acts in a way that makes an impression on you , for you will use all three of these elements to create your sketch.

Here are some other suggestions to help you choose a good subject:

1. Your subject must be a real person, not imaginary or fictitious.

2. Your subject can be a relative (other than a parent, brother, sister, or someone who lives in the same house with you).

3. You do not have to know the subject personally, as long as you are able to observe him or her.

☑ Keeping these requirements in mind, list below three people that you think would be good subjects for your character sketch. Put a star by the name of the person who interests you the most.

1. _____

2. _____

3. _____

A SUBJECT for a character sketch should be someone who stands out in your mind in some way.

Freewriting to Get Started

You can use freewriting to begin your character sketch. When you freewrite, you write freely and quickly. You can write sentences, phrases, or words. Don't worry about writing correctly or getting your words "just right." Your goal is simply to get a lot of words and ideas down on paper.

Before you begin to freewrite, close your eyes and think of the person you have chosen to write about. What image comes to mind? What is the person wearing, doing, and saying? When you think about this person, what words come to mind?

On the lines below, take about five minutes to freewrite for your character sketch. Write quickly and without stopping.

_____

_____

_____

_____

_____

_____

_____

_____

_____

_____

_____

_____

_____

_____

_____

_____

_____

_____

_____

_____

_____

_____

_____

_____

_____

_____

_____

_____

✓ If possible, before the next lesson, try to observe the subject of your character sketch. Take a small notebook and record specific examples of appearance, behavior, and speech.

PREWRITING: Getting Ready to Write

Using Details

In addition to specific information, a good character sketch includes details that help readers see mental pictures. Read the following description:

> Russ Becker was a short but muscular baseball coach. Although he got upset when his team played badly, he was always kind to the players.

Do you have a mental picture of Coach Becker? Does he interest you? If one of your answers is "no" or "I'm not sure," you probably need more details to help you see and understand the character. To see what a difference details can make, read the following passage .

> Coach Becker seemed even shorter than usual as he squatted on the steps of the dugout, chewing gum and doodling on the lineup sheet. When the pinch hitter struck out, Coach broke his pencil and chomped his gum as if he had a grudge against it. His muscles bulged, like Popeye's after a can of spinach. But his eyes remained kind, and he gently patted the disappointed batter's shoulder.

Now do you have a clearer mental picture of Coach Becker? Answer the questions below.

1. What details tell us what Coach looked like?

   _____

   _____

2. What details show (rather than tell) us that he was upset?

   _____

   _____

3. What details does the writer use to show that the coach was kind?

   _____

   _____

✓ Now, on the lines below, make a list of details you could use to describe the person you selected for your character sketch. Choose details that would help your readers understand the person's appearance, behavior, speech, and achievements.

_____

_____

A good CHARACTER SKETCH includes specific facts and details to help readers see and understand the person. Remember: show, don't tell.

Gathering Observations and Impressions

You know that specific details bring a character sketch to life. To come up with those details, you need to gather and organize your observations and impressions of the person you're writing about. You can gather these observations and impressions from various sources, including:

- The freewriting you did in the previous lesson
- Any notes you have taken while observing the subject of your character sketch
- Your memory

Joe decided to write about his neighbor, Mr. Diaz. He recorded the following facts:

1. Appearance

   5'10" tall, bald with a black mustache, skinny (about 150 lbs.), dark tanned skin, wears a sport coat to work

2. Behavior

walks quickly with head up, often works in his garden, very quiet, almost seems shy

3. Speech

greets people with "A good day to you," has a slight Spanish accent

4. Achievements

gives vegetables to everyone in the neighborhood, volunteers at the library, picks up groceries for older neighbors

☑ Now it's your turn to record your observations and impressions of your subject. Use your memory and any notes you have already written. Use the chart on the following page to organize your observations and impressions in these categories:

- Appearance (how the person looks)
- Behavior (how the person acts)
- Speech (how the person talks)
- Achievements (what the person has accomplished)

You do not have to write in complete sentences. You can write in the space provided or on separate sheets. Try to write at least two items in each category— more would be better. After you finish, go back later and see if you can add more specific details in each category.

Appearance

_____

_____

_____

_____

_____

_____

Behavior

_____

_____

_____

_____

_____

_____

Name of Subject

_____

_____

Speech

_____

_____

_____

_____

_____

Achievements

_____

_____

_____

_____

_____

PREWRITING: Organizing the Character Sketch

You have recorded many observations and impressions for your character sketch, and you are just about ready to write the draft. A bit more planning, however, will make it easier for you to write the draft.

The Main Impression

In life, people are complex. Depending on the situation, they can act in very different ways. They have thoughts and feelings that other people never see. And yet, even though people are complex, they often make a *main impression* on us.

The main impression is the single trait or quality you think of first when you think of a certain person. "Sheila is so determined; she never gives up. Billy is the quiet one; you never know what he's thinking. Fred is so funny! He has a joke for every occasion."

When you write a character sketch, you want to tell a lot about the person, but you also want to leave your reader with a main impression. The main impression is the quality you want your reader to remember after he or she finishes reading the character sketch.

For example, look again on pages 46 and 47 at the notes that Joe wrote about his neighbor, Mr. Diaz. When Joe reviewed his notes, he knew that he wanted to leave his readers with the main impression of Mr. Diaz as *a kind and generous man.*

You have written many notes about the appearance, behavior, speech, and achievements of the person you're writing about. Review your notes, and as you do, think about the main impression you want to leave with your reader. Write it in the space below:

_____

_____

A Paragraph Outline

You have written outlines for reports and research papers. In those outlines, you used Roman numerals and numbers to organize main topics and subtopics.

For a character sketch, you can use a simpler outline, called a paragraph outline. To make a paragraph outline, you write a phrase or sentence to describe what you think will be the main point of each paragraph.

Here is Joe's paragraph outline for his character sketch of Mr. Diaz:

1. Introduction—identify Mr. Diaz: kind and generous neighbor
2. Appearance, behavior, and speech: try to make reader see and hear Mr. Diaz
3. Kind and generous actions: picks up groceries for older neighbors
4. Volunteers at library
5. Conclusion—a kind and generous man, a good neighbor to all

If you want to, use Joe's outline as a model for the paragraph outline for your character sketch. Here is the general plan of Joe's outline:

Paragraph 1: Introduction: Show the person doing something that supports the main impression.

Paragraph 2: Describe appearance, speech, and behavior. Help your reader see the person.

Paragraph 3: Example #1 of an action that supports the main impression

Paragraph 4: Example #2 of an action that supports the main impression

Paragraph 5: Conclusion: Reinforce the main impression.

☑ Review your notes and think about the main points you want to make. Then prepare a paragraph outline for your character sketch. You can use the space on the next page or a separate sheet of paper.

DRAFTING: Writing the Body

You have finished your preparations and are ready to write. As you do, keep in mind that a character sketch (like many other kinds of writing) has three main parts: the introduction, the body, and the conclusion.

The main part of your paper is called its BODY. It contains the most information about your character. In this section you show the reader why your character is so interesting. You can do this best by using specific details.

Show, Don't Tell

You will definitely want to describe your character's physical appearance. When Ron wrote his sketch, he described his neighbor in the following way:

> Mrs. Simms is an interesting older person. She loves gardening and children. She dresses in bright colors and wears stylish clothes.

Can you clearly picture what Mrs. Simms looks like? Do you know what makes her different from other people? Ron can improve his description by *showing* rather than *telling* us about his neighbor in the following ways:

1. By using specific descriptive words
2. By using figures of speech
3. By showing how the person behaved at certain times
4. By including dialogue that is unique to the character

SHOW, don't tell, the reader about your subject by using specific details and examples of behavior in the body of your character sketch.

Using Specific Descriptive Words

Mr. Tom bent stiffly over the tomato plant. His rough, wrinkled hands carefully tied the long, spindly vines to the wooden stakes. His dark eyes narrowed as he struggled to tie the knots. He stood up slowly. Even when he was standing, he seemed to be bent over. As he pushed back his tattered hat and wiped his brow, wisps of white hair escaped. With his stiff fingers, he buttoned the frayed gray sweater that he seemed to wear every day. Then he slowly bent down to take care of another plant.

Can you picture that scene? Details make the difference. Find some words in the last paragraph that describe the following:

Mr. Tom's body _____

Mr. Tom's clothes _____

Mr. Tom's tomato plants _____

Now write some descriptive words and phrases you could use in the body of your own character sketch.

_____

_____

_____

_____

_____

Using Figures of Speech

Figures of speech are expressions used differently from their normal meaning. Like descriptive words, they are used to create pictures in the reader's mind. Two figures of speech are the SIMILE and the METAPHOR.

Both similes and metaphors compare unlike things. A simile uses *like* or *as* in the comparison. For example:

Simile: In an argument, Mr. Johnson is *like a bulldog*. He grabs hold of an idea and won't let go.

Metaphor: Mr. Johnson *is a bulldog* in an argument. He grabs hold of an idea and won't let go.

Look for similes and metaphors as you read the following paragraph:

Coach Becker is a short man, but his muscles are like cannonballs. During his years of coaching, the lines at the corners of his eyes have grown from sparrow tracks to highways. When he squints at the outfield, he scrunches up his face like a bulldog. He can be as tough as he looks when he needs to, but is usually as gentle as a teddy bear.

On the lines below, tell whether each word or phrase is used as a metaphor or a simile in the previous paragraph about Coach Becker. Also write what is being described.

cannonballs _____

sparrow tracks to highways _____

bulldog _____

teddy bear _____

☑ On the next two lines, write one simile and one metaphor you could use in your character sketch.

_____

_____

Showing Behavior

It is better to show than to tell the reader about your character. Use specific examples of your subject's behavior to make him or her seem more real. Read the following paragraph from Joe's character sketch about Mr. Diaz:

Mr. Diaz is not a young man, but he is in good health, and he helps his older neighbors. For example, he helps Mrs. Santini, whose eyes are so weak that she is no longer allowed to drive a car. Every Saturday morning, Mr. Diaz stops at Mrs. Santini's house to pick up her grocery list. And every Saturday afternoon, he returns to the house with a full sack in each arm. He helps Mrs. Santini put the groceries away in the pantry and the

refrigerator. As he leaves, Mrs. Santini always tries to give him five dollars for his help. Mr. Diaz always takes the five dollars, folds it twice, and puts it back in Mrs. Santini's hand. He places his hand on hers and says, "You send this to your grandchildren." Then he bows politely and drives off to help another neighbor.

Joe doesn't just *tell* us that Mr. Diaz is kind and generous. He shows us a detailed example of Mr. Diaz's kind and generous behavior.

On the lines below, list two examples you can write about to *show* your subject's character.

_____

_____

_____

✓ Now, on your own paper, write the first draft of the body of your character sketch. Try to make your character seem real by using specific descriptive details, figures of speech, examples of behavior, and dialogue. Use all the notes you've made and follow your paragraph outline. Double-space when you write.

DRAFTING: Writing the Introduction and Conclusion

Writing the Introduction

The INTRODUCTION, or beginning, of your paper is important. It must be interesting enough to make the reader want to go on reading.

WRITER'S WORKSHOP

A good INTRODUCTION makes the reader want to continue reading.

Read the introductions below and follow the instructions at the top of the next page.

A. Some people go through life like leaves blown by the wind. They skitter from one place to another, never seeming to belong anywhere. Sometimes they stop for a while, but then the wind blows, and they're off again. That's the way it was with Sparky.

B. Sara is a really neat person. She has many interesting qualities. Some of these are the way she speaks, the way she looks, and the way she acts.

C. There he was, sitting in Joe's candy store across the street. He caught my eye just as I opened the door of the department store. A man of sixty, he was wearing outdated clothes with holes that revealed his brown wrinkled skin. He was keeping himself busy by folding a candy wrapper into various shapes, as if unable to decide which he preferred.

On the lines below, tell which of the passages you liked best. Which one made you want to go on reading? Explain your answer.

_____

_____

_____

When Lisa read the same passages, she chose Introduction A as the one that "hooked" her. She wanted to know who Sparky was, what he looked like, and why he was so restless. The writer had tempted her by creating a bit of a mystery.

Sam, however, chose Introduction C. The description of the man caught his interest. He wanted to know more about this character.

You may want to use one of these two methods (*mystery* or a *fascinating description*) as you write the introduction to your character sketch. Use the space below to make notes for your introduction.

_____

_____

_____

_____

_____

_____

✓ Now write your introduction on another sheet of paper. Remember that you want to "hook" readers so that they want to go on reading. Remember also that you are writing a DRAFT. Concentrate on getting your ideas down on paper. Don't worry too much about spelling and other mistakes at this time. That will come later. Skip lines as you write so that you will have space to make changes.

Writing the Conclusion

A character sketch without an ending is like a mystery story with no solution. While your CONCLUSION does not have to be long, your sketch won't seem complete without it.

WRITER'S WORKSHOP

The CONCLUSION sums up the writer's feelings about the subject of a character sketch.

Here is the first conclusion Ron wrote: *I really like Mrs. Simms and I'm glad that she is my neighbor.* Then he remembered the "show-don't-tell" rule and decided to try again. In his second conclusion, Ron also tried to explain how he felt about his neighbor and the effect she'd had on him.

> Mrs. Simms is as kind to kids as she is to grown-ups. If your friend insults you or you're worried about a big test, she always has time for encouragement, served up with milk and cookies. She has taught me what "good neighbor" means.

Use the lines below to plan your conclusion.

How do I feel about my subject? _____

_____

What effect (if any) has he or she had on my life? _____

_____

What detail or example could I use to illustrate my feeling? _____

_____

☑ On your own paper, write the conclusion for your character sketch. Make sure the reader knows exactly how you feel about your subject and what effect, if any, he or she has had upon your life. Use your notes from above. Double–space to leave room for revisions.

REVISING: Improving Content and Organization/Checking Sentences

When you have completed your first draft, you are ready for an important step: revising (changing and improving) your character sketch. Very few good writers are satisfied with their first tries. For example, look at the following section of William H. Armstrong's manuscript for his book *Sounder*. Notice the changes Mr. Armstrong has made. If you compare the manuscript with the book (near the beginning), you'll see that the author made even more changes later.

Notice also that William Armstrong did not make a fresh copy of his manuscript each time he revised. You too can make changes right on your first draft.

Using Dialogue

Here is part of a paragraph that Joe wrote in his character sketch about Mr. Diaz:

As he leaves, Mrs. Santini always tries to give him five dollars for his help. Mr. Diaz always takes the five dollars, folds it twice, and puts it back in Mrs. Santini's hand. He places his hand on hers and says, "You send this to your grandchildren." Then he bows politely and drives off to help another neighbor.

In that paragraph, Joe included a bit of DIALOGUE. Dialogue is the conversation and speech of characters. Dialogue is a form of showing rather than telling. It can help bring a character to life. Compare these two sentences:

- He places his hand on hers and says, "You send this to your grandchildren."
- He places his hand on hers and tells her to send the money to her grandchildren.

Do you see how the sentence with dialogue helps us *hear* Mr. Diaz? It makes him a more real character.

Here are some ways dialogue can help:

1. Dialogue makes a piece of writing *look* inviting and readable. People are usually interested in what others say.

2. Dialogue can help reveal the character of a person. For example: "Don't tease that cat, son. It's frightened."

3. An expression that someone uses frequently becomes a characteristic of that person, a way in which he or she is different from others. For example, when Ann's neighbor came to visit, he always said, "What's cookin' today?"

When you write DIALOGUE, remember these three rules:

1. Put the words each speaker says within quotation marks.

2. Punctuation marks such as commas and periods almost always go *inside* the quotation marks.

3. Begin a new paragraph each time a different person starts to speak.

✓ Now, go back to the draft of your character sketch. Can you add dialogue to bring your subject to life?

Revising for Content and Organization

When you revise, you go back through your draft and try to make it better. You can correct errors in spelling or punctuation if you see them, but don't focus on correcting errors. You'll do that later. Instead, focus on the *content*—the main points in your essay. Also consider the *organization*—the order in which you present the main points.

✓ Use the checklist below to indicate changes you need to make as you revise your character sketch.

	Good	Could Be Better
1. Does my introduction catch the reader's attention?	____	____
2. Have I made my character interesting to my readers?	____	____
3. Does the body contain specific examples of my subject's behavior? Do I show rather than tell?	____	____
4. Do the paragraphs make sense in the order in which I organized them? Can a reader easily follow what I have to say?	____	____
5. Does the conclusion let the reader know how I feel about the subject?	____	____

Checking for Sentence Fragments and Run-ons

In order to be understood by readers, your thoughts must be clearly expressed in proper sentences. Incomplete sentences (fragments) and sentences that run together (run-ons) are errors to look out for.

Fragments

Make sure that each sentence expresses a complete thought. Does each sentence contain a subject and a predicate? (Remember, the SUBJECT tells who or what the sentence is about; the PREDICATE contains the verb and all the words that follow it.) Read each group of words below and put checks next to those that are fragments.

_____ 1. Sue has a new headphone radio. _____ 5. The snow fell.

_____ 2. Trying to make pizza. _____ 6. His old car.

_____ 3. When Bill slides into second. _____ 7. Who came?

_____ 4. Ben bought a banana split. _____ 8. Out of the shadows.

Four groups of words above are not complete thoughts. Rewrite these groups below, adding words to make them complete sentences.

1. _____

2. _____

3. _____

4. _____

Run-ons

A RUN-ON SENTENCE contains two or more complete thoughts, improperly joined together. For example, here is a sentence that Joe wrote: *Al loved to laugh, he was always telling jokes*. What is wrong with Joe's sentence?

When you find two or more complete thoughts improperly joined together, you may correct the error in one of these ways:

1. Place a period after the first complete thought. Begin the first word of the second complete thought with a capital letter.

2. Put a semicolon (;) between the two thoughts, if they are closely related to each other.

3. Separate the thoughts with commas, and begin the second thought with a conjunction (a word such as *and, or, but,* or *so* that joins thoughts together).

Correct Joe's run-on sentence (from above), using each of those three methods.

1. _____

2. _____

3. _____

☑ Now check your character sketch for fragments and run-on sentences. If you find any, correct them.

REVISING: Choosing the Best Words

Words can be as dull and muddy as a puddle, or they can sparkle like a clear mountain stream. You can make your character sketch both clear and sparkling by using just the right words. Today you will focus on conjunctions, adjectives, and verbs.

Proofreading Symbols

Before you begin, take a few minutes to review these proofreading marks. They might come in handy today as you revise your character sketch.

¶	Start a new paragraph	preferred.¶An emotional man
℘	Delete (take out)	store.℘ An old man of sixty
∧	Insert (put in)	as∧opened the door
◡	Delete space	store. An old◡man of sixty,
#	Add space	store. An old#man of sixty,
◯	Misspelled word	(stoar.) An old man of sixty,
⌣	Switch places	store. An man⌣old of sixty,
⊙	Add period	store⊙ An old man of sixty,
⌃	Add comma	An old man of sixty⌃ he was
⌄	Add apostrophe	sitting in Joe⌄s candy store
=	Capitalize	store. =an old man of sixty,
/	Use small letter	store. An Øld man of sixty,
⌐◯	Move circled word to point of arrow	store. An man of sixty(old)

Using the Best Conjunction

What is wrong with the paragraph below?

Mrs. Simms is my neighbor and she is a great lady. She likes kids and she likes to bake cookies and that is a good combination. She listens to us and she is always sympathetic.

Did you say that the paragraph contains too many *ands*? That is a common problem. The word *and* is just one of many useful conjunctions. Your writing will be more interesting if you choose a conjunction that fits the sentence best. Here are some examples:

Mrs. Simms is a good neighbor and she always has time for kids.

Mrs. Simms is a good neighbor because she always has time for kids.

In the first sentence, the word *and* tells us only that the two thoughts are connected. In the second sentence, the word *because* tells us *how* the thoughts are connected. It tells us that the second thought will answer the question *why* or *in what way* Mrs. Simms is a good neighbor.

Different conjunctions signal different relationships between thoughts. *Because* and *so* signal that one thought gives a reason for the other, as in the sentence above. Here are some other conjunctions with their meanings:

when, after, before—indicate that one thought tells when the other happened
When Mrs. Simms saw us coming, she got out the cookie jar.

but, although—used when one thought is in contrast with the other
I like chocolate chips best, but Sue likes gingerbread.

if—used when one thought expresses a condition for the other
If I ever have kids for neighbors, I'm going to be like Mrs. Simms.

All of the sentences below include the conjunction *and*. Change each sentence, using a different conjunction *(as, when, after, so, because, but, if,* or *although)* to make the meaning clearer. (Also change punctuation and capitalization as needed.) The first sentence has been done as an example.

1. *After*
   We spent a few days practicing ~~and~~ we learned to ski.

2. The train pulled into the station and the noise was deafening.

3. Mr. Tom was rich and he lived like a hermit.

4. We liked to talk with Mr. Diaz and we visited him often.

5. We didn't ski that day and it was not very cold.

✓ Now check your character sketch to see if you can improve it by changing some conjunctions.

Using Specific Adjectives

Some adjectives are dull and general *(tall, old, big, small, weak)*. Others are bright and specific *(wrinkled, shimmering, clumsy)*. Which sentence below creates a clearer picture?

The legs of the newborn giraffe were weak.

The legs of the newborn giraffe were wobbly.

Beside each general adjective below, write a specific one that creates a clearer picture.

noisy _____   tall _____

colorful _____   nice _____

slow _____   bad _____

The adjectives you use in writing should appeal to all of the five senses—taste, touch, hearing, sight, and smell.

✓ Look back through your draft. Do you see any weak, general adjectives such as *good, nice,* or *big*? Replace them with strong, specific adjectives.

Using the Active Voice

Another way to make your writing strong and lively is to use the ACTIVE VOICE whenever you can. In the active voice, the subject of the sentence does the acting. For example: *Sam drove the Thunderbird.* In the PASSIVE VOICE, the subject receives the action of the verb. For example: *The Thunderbird was driven by Sam.* Which of the sentences below seems strongest?

The cold temperature was felt by Rosco.

Rosco felt the cold.

Change each verb below from passive to active voice. The first sentence has been done as an example.

1. A snakeskin vest was worn by the wrestler.

   The wrestler wore a snakeskin vest.

2. The dusty elephant was bathed by the trainer.

   _____

3. A home run was hit by the pinch hitter.

   _____

4. The award was presented to Ted by Mr. Packard.

   _____

☑ Check your own character sketch to be sure it uses the active voice whenever possible.

PROOFREADING/PUBLISHING: The Final Check

☑ Mechanics, astronauts, doctors, and writers all use checklists to be sure their work is in order. Before you make the final copy of your character sketch, use the list below to be sure your sketch is as good as you can make it.

Content

_____ My introduction will catch the attention of the reader.

_____ The body of my paper contains specific details that show rather than tell.

_____ My conclusion sums up how I feel about the subject.

Correct Writing

_____ All of my sentences have correct structure (no run-ons or fragments).

_____ I begin a new paragraph whenever there is a new idea, place, time, location, or speaker.

_____ I use adjectives and action verbs to create mental pictures.

_____ Most of my verbs are in the active voice.

_____ Capitalization, punctuation, and spelling in my paper are correct.

If there are no blank spaces on your checklist, you are ready to make your final copy.

If you have given your best effort to your character sketch, you should be pleased with yourself. Congratulations! You have become a portrait painter who uses words instead of paints and brushes.

WRITING A RESEARCH PAPER

PREWRITING: Choosing and Narrowing a Topic

Earlier this year, you wrote a research paper. What was the topic of your research paper?

Research papers are a very important kind of writing. So, since "practice makes perfect," you will write another one.

A research paper is a big project. The key to doing it well is to take one step at a time. Let's review the main steps in writing a research paper:

Choose and narrow a topic.

Make a list of possible sources.

Fill out a bibliography card for each source.

Take plenty of good notes.

Organize your notes.

Write a thesis statement.

Make an outline.

Write your first draft.

Revise your paper.

Prepare a bibliography.

Prepare the final copy.

Choosing a Topic

For the topic of this research paper, choose something you have been studying this year that you would like to know more about. Did something you studied in History or Science really grab your interest? In Art or Music, did you meet a painter or composer you'd like to know more about? Is there an author you'd like to learn about?

Here are some topics you might have studied in your other courses.

Science

Water pollution and conservation

The effect of "El Niño" on climate

The "greenhouse effect"

Art

Sculptures by Degas

Navajo blankets

John James Audubon

History

Indians of the Pacific Northwest

The Lost Colony

Thomas Jefferson

The Civil War

Literature

Phillis Whitney

Shakespeare and the Globe Theater

Louisa May Alcott

Instead of choosing a topic that comes directly from your studies, you might choose a topic that grows out of what you have studied. For example, a student interested in Science lessons about climate might write a research paper on what is required to become a meteorologist.

Begin by reviewing what you have studied in your other courses this year. Look back through any notebooks, papers, or readings you have collected. Skim the pages to get ideas.

Use the space below to brainstorm about possible topics. As you review your notebooks and other materials, write notes on any topics you might be able to use for a research paper.

_____

_____

_____

_____

Take a look at the ideas you brainstormed. In the spaces below, write the two that interest you most.

1. _____

2. _____

Narrowing Your Topic

If your topic is too broad, you will need to narrow it so you won't be overwhelmed by all the information you might find.

For example, Paul wanted to know more about the Civil War, but "the Civil War" is too broad to use as a topic for a research paper. Paul asked himself: "What in particular about the Civil War would I like to know more about?" As he looked through his notes and books, he remembered being interested in the development of early ironclad ships. He decided to do his research on the Civil War battle between the *Monitor* and the *Merrimack*.

Sometimes you find a way to narrow a topic when you first start doing research. For example, Rosa knew that she wanted to learn more about Thomas Jefferson. She knew that was too broad a topic, so she started reading a short biography of Jefferson. This reading led her to narrow her topic. She decided to write about Thomas Jefferson as an inventor.

Read over your possible topics. Put a star by the one that interests you most. Is it too broad? Like Paul, do you need to ask, "What *in particular* about this topic would I like to know more about?" Like Rosa, do you need to do a bit of reading before you can narrow the topic?

Once you have chosen a topic and narrowed it, write it here:

_____

_____

Remember, this is your *working* topic. You might change it after you have done more research.

PREWRITING: Identifying Sources

Now that you have decided on a topic, you need to find sources of information about your topic. At the library, you can look for encyclopedias, books, and magazines. You can also search the Internet.

Using the Library

At the library, you can find several kinds of sources, including books, magazines, and reference materials. The challenge is to narrow down the huge number of sources. As you go through the library's catalog, make a list of sources that appear promising or useful for your research paper.

As you make your list, here are the facts you need to take down for each kind of source:

Source	Where to Look	Facts Needed to Find
1. Circulating books	card catalog or computer catalog	call number, title, author
2. Magazines	*Reader's Guide* or computer catalog	title, volume number, publication date, page numbers
3. Reference materials	card catalog or computer catalog	call number, title, volume number, page numbers

Here is how Rosa listed three promising sources for her research paper on Thomas Jefferson. The first two are books, and the third is a periodical.

> *J92 Jefferson Meet Thomas Jefferson by Marvin Barrett*
>
> *J92 Jefferson Thomas Jefferson: His Many Talents by Johanna Johnston*
>
> *Cobblestone, Vol. 10 No. 9, Sept. 1989, pages 22-26*

List five sources that might contain useful information on your topic. If you want to list more sources, use a separate sheet.

1. _____

_____

2. _____

_____

3. _____

_____

4. _____

_____

5. _____

_____

Using the Internet

With the guidance of an adult, you can also search the Internet for information on your topic.

The Internet has a lot of information, but you have to be very careful to be sure you are getting good information. Make sure your Internet sources are trustworthy. In general, you can rely on the information in government websites (such as NASA's website) and the websites of well-known museums.

When you find a reliable source with good information, write down the name of the site, the URL (the Internet address) of the specific page or pages you use, and the date you visit the site. For example:

Name of Site: Monticello—The Home of Thomas Jefferson
URL: http://www.monticello.org/jefferson/sunrise/home.html
Date: February 15, 2003

Exploring Sources

Once you have prepared a list of possible sources, you need to find them in your library. Quickly scan each one to see if it will be useful for your topic. For a periodical, quickly skim the article. For books:

- Check the table of contents to see if a chapter or chapters deal with your topic.
- Check the index to see if your topic is listed.
- Skim the relevant pages to see if the information is useful and is written at a good reading level for you.

Preparing Bibliography Cards

For each source that you plan to use for your paper, prepare a bibliography card. Your bibliography cards will help you keep track of your sources, and later make it easy for you to put together the bibliography for your paper.

Here is the information you need to include on bibliography cards for different types of sources:

- Books: call number, author's name, title, city of publication, name of the publisher, and date of publication
- Magazines: author (if known), title of article, name of magazine, date of publication, volume number (if available), and page numbers
- Encyclopedias (and other reference books): author (if known), title of article, name of encyclopedia, date of the edition, volume number, and page numbers of the article

Here are three bibliography cards that Rosa prepared:

Book:

Call number	J92 Jefferson
Author	Johnston, Johanna
Title	Thomas Jefferson: His Many Talents
Publication facts	New York: Dodd, Mead, 1961

Periodical:

Author	Zuber, Shari Lyn
Title	"A Man of Many Ideas"
Publication facts	<u>Cobblestone</u>, Vol. 10 No. 9, Sept. 1989, pages 22-26

Encyclopedia:

Author	Cunningham, Noble E., Jr.
Title	"Thomas Jefferson"
Publication facts	<u>World Book Encyclopedia</u> 2002 ed. Vol. 11, pages 76-87

☑ Fill out a separate bibliography card for each source you use in your research.

LESSONS 3-4

PREWRITING: Taking Notes

Once you have your sources, you need to take notes. If you take plenty of good notes, it will be much easier to write your research paper. (That's why this task has been given two lessons' worth of time in this unit.)

Here are some reminders on taking notes for your research paper.

- Use a new note card for each piece of information.
- At the top left of the card, list the subtopic of the information you are recording. For example, for her research paper on Thomas Jefferson as an inventor, Rosa wrote this subtopic at the top of a note card: *Jefferson's moving chair*.
- In general, summarize and paraphrase the information. In other words, only take down the main points and put them in your own words.
- If you write down the exact words of the author of the source, be sure to enclose the words in quotation marks. Quotation marks show that these are someone else's words, not yours. It is very important to use quotation marks when you use another writer's words, in order to avoid *plagiarism*, which is stealing someone else's words or ideas.
- On the top right of each card, list the author and the page number on which you found the information. If the author was not named, write down another piece of information that will help you identify the source, such as the main words of the title.

Here is one of Rosa's note cards:

Jefferson's moving chair   Johnston, p. 98
   Jefferson designed it, built by the cabinet-maker at Monticello
   He wanted a chair that could move around so he could reach
      books to the side or turn to see people who wanted to talk with him
   Small wheels attached to the legs of a comfortable chair
   Was called "Jefferson's whirl-i-gig"

PREWRITING: Planning Your Research Paper

You've taken many notes from your sources. Now it's time to plan your paper by arranging your note cards into separate stacks according to their content.

You will probably have three or four stacks when you finish sorting your cards. For example, Rosa had one stack of cards on "Jefferson's copying machine," another stack on "Jefferson's moving chair," and other stacks on other inventions.

When you finish, you may find you have cards you did not use, or that you need more information. This often happens in doing research. Put aside the cards you did not use. Don't throw them out—you might use them later. Do additional research to find any information you still need.

Writing a Thesis Statement

A thesis statement expresses the main idea of a research paper.

Sometimes, your main idea changes while you are doing research. Look back to the topic you wrote on page 70. Based on the research you have done, do you need to change it?

Here is the thesis statement Rosa wrote for her research paper:

Thomas Jefferson, the author of the Declaration of Independence and our third president, was also an inventor who was always thinking of new and better ways to make things work.

Write your thesis statement—the main idea of your paper—on the lines below. In the rest of your paper, you will prove your thesis statement. The subtopics you have from sorting your cards should all support your thesis statement.

_____

_____

_____

Making an Outline

An outline can help you plan and write your paper. At the top of a separate sheet of paper, write your thesis statement, and then write your outline below it. As you write your outline, keep looking back to your thesis statement to make sure that all of your points support the main idea expressed in the thesis statement.

Here are some reminders about how to prepare an outline.

- Your outline should contain at least three MAIN TOPICS. These are the major subject areas you wrote at the top of your note cards. The main topics in an outline follow Roman numerals and periods (I., II., III., IV.).

- Each main topic may be divided into SUBTOPICS. Subtopics contain more specific information about the subjects under which they are listed. Subtopics follow capital letters and periods (A., B., C.). Each subtopic must contain at least two parts (at least A. and B.).

- Under a subtopic you can list SPECIFIC FACTS that follow Arabic numerals and periods (1., 2., 3.). You must list at least two specific facts (1., 2.), but you can list more.

Here is *part* of the outline for Rosa's research paper:

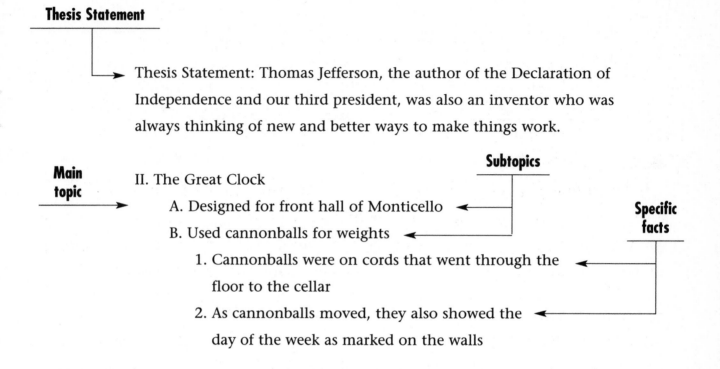

Thesis Statement

Thesis Statement: Thomas Jefferson, the author of the Declaration of Independence and our third president, was also an inventor who was always thinking of new and better ways to make things work.

Main topic

Subtopics

II. The Great Clock

A. Designed for front hall of Monticello

B. Used cannonballs for weights

Specific facts

1. Cannonballs were on cords that went through the floor to the cellar

2. As cannonballs moved, they also showed the day of the week as marked on the walls

✓ Your outline should include all the important information you want to include in your research paper. Write the outline for your report on a separate sheet.

DRAFTING: Writing the Body

Now you're ready to write the body of your research paper. Start with the body, and then come back in the next lesson to work on the introduction and conclusion.

As you work, remember:

- Place your note cards in front of you in the order in which you will use them. The order should follow your outline.
- Follow your outline. You might find you need to update your outline as you write. If so, that's all right. Let your outline guide you, not restrict you.
- Every paragraph in the body of your paper should be about a single main idea. This single main idea should be announced in the topic sentence, which is usually the first sentence.
- The rest of the sentences in the paragraph should support the topic sentence with facts and details.
- Double-space to leave room for revisions later.

Gather your note cards, check your outline, and start your engine! As you write the body of your research paper, keep in mind that this is a draft. Don't worry too much about getting every word and punctuation mark just right. For now, focus on getting your ideas down in order.

On your mark . . . get set . . . go!

DRAFTING: Writing the Introduction and Conclusion

The Introduction

The introduction has two jobs:

1. To get the reader's attention
2. To preview the content of the paper

Your introduction should contain your thesis statement, or some version of it, since the thesis statement announces the main idea of your paper.

There are several ways to interest your reader in what he will be reading. Here are some suggestions.

- Begin with a description. For example, in her paper on Thomas Jefferson as an inventor, Rosa could briefly describe one of Jefferson's curious inventions.

- Begin with a question. Your reader will want to read on to find out the answer.

- Begin with a quotation. If you have a great quotation that will catch your reader's attention, use that to begin your paper.

- Begin with a startling fact. If you run across a fact or statistic that fascinates you, you could begin with that. It might fascinate your reader, too.

Here is the introduction to Rosa's research paper. You can see how she has used a version of her thesis sentence at the end of the introduction.

When people think of Thomas Jefferson, they might think of ink flowing from a quill pen as he wrote the Declaration of Independence. They probably do not think of pasta squeezing out of a macaroni-making machine. After visiting Europe, however, Jefferson returned to the United States and sketched a design for a macaroni maker. Although he is best known as the author of the Declaration of Independence who later became our third president, Thomas

Jefferson was also an inventor whose curious mind was always thinking of new and better ways to make things work.

✓ Now write the draft of your introduction. Use one of the ways above, if you wish. You can also try writing more than one introduction and see which one you like best. Double-space to leave room for revisions.

The Conclusion

In this last part of your paper, you wrap up what you learned. Often, a conclusion includes some brief reminders about the main points of the paper. If possible, give your readers something to think about. You may want to challenge them to act or inspire them to find out more about what they have learned through reading your paper.

✓ Now write the draft of your conclusion to your research paper. Double-space to leave room for revisions.

REVISING: Improving Your Research Paper

You have written a complete draft of your research paper, from beginning to end. Now it's time to look at your draft with a critical eye and see if you can make it even better.

One good way to begin revising is by reading your draft to an adult. As you read, you may notice sentences you want to change or take out, or you might see where you need to add more information. If you see places to improve, make a mark on the draft, and then continue reading aloud. Then go back to the passages you have marked and revise the draft.

Use this checklist to help you revise your research paper. Go over each point. If the item needs work, mark "Needs Work." Then make the revisions, and when you are satisfied, check "Yes."

What You Need to Check: **Needs Work   Yes**

Introduction
The opening gets the reader's attention.   _____ _____
The introduction tells the reader what my report is about.   _____ _____

Body
All the paragraphs in the report support the thesis statement. _____ _____
The paragraphs flow in an order that makes sense to the reader. _____ _____
Each paragraph has a topic sentence.   _____ _____
Each paragraph has enough facts and details to
  support the topic sentence.   _____ _____
In each paragraph, every sentence is clearly related to
  the topic sentence.   _____ _____

What You Need to Check: Needs Work   Yes

Conclusion

The conclusion tells the reader what I learned.   _____   _____

The conclusion leaves the reader with

  something to think about.   _____   _____

✓   When you revise, you have to imagine you are the reader. Does this paper interest you? Does it provide enough information? Can you follow it easily from one paragraph to the next?

Try to find at least three ways to improve your research paper.

Compiling a Bibliography

In a research paper, it is very important to let your readers know where you got your information. That is why you identify all the sources you use in a bibliography.

It should be easy for you to do this because you have already written bibliography cards. Gather the cards for all the sources you used in your research paper.

Write or type your bibliography on a separate sheet of paper, titled *Bibliography*. Double-space your entries, listing them in alphabetical order by the author's name. If no author is identified, use the first main word of the title. (Don't count "A," "An," or "The" in a title.)

Only include the sources you used. If you ended up not using a source, then do not list it in your bibliography.

Here are some model bibliography entries that you can follow:

Books

Johnston, Johanna. <u>Thomas Jefferson: His Many Talents</u>. New York: Dodd, Mead, 1961.

Davis, Todd and Marc Frey. <u>The New Book of U. S. Presidents: A Young Reader's Guide to the Presidency</u>. Philadelphia: Running Press, 2001.

Periodicals

Zuber, Shari Lyn. "A Man of Many Ideas." <u>Cobblestone</u> Vol. 10 No. 9, September 1989, pages 22-26.

Encyclopedias

Cunningham, Noble E., Jr. "Thomas Jefferson." <u>World Book Encyclopedia</u>. 2002 ed. Vol. 11, pages 76-87.

Internet Sources

"Monticello—The Home of Thomas Jefferson." 15 February 2003.
   <http://www.monticello.org/jefferson/sunrise/home.html>

"Thomas Jefferson." <u>The New Book of Knowledge</u>. Grolier Online. 16 February
2003. <http://go.grolier.com/>

Here are some details to keep in mind:

- If a book has more than one author, use the last name of the first author listed in the book. For the second and third authors, write the first name first. If there are more than three authors, only use the first listed author, and after his name write *et al.* which is a Latin abbreviation meaning "and others."
- Notice that the titles of articles are in quotation marks, and the titles of books are underlined. (If you are using a word processor, then instead of underlining book titles, put them in italics.)
- In the samples of Internet sources, notice the style for writing dates: (day) (month) (year), for example: 21 March 2003.
- Begin each bibliography entry at the left margin of the page. If the entry runs to a second or third line, indent all lines after the first.

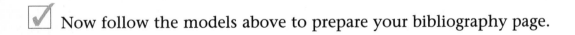 Now follow the models above to prepare your bibliography page.

PROOFREADING/PUBLISHING: Preparing the Final Copy

You're almost finished. You need to think of a title for your paper. Then all you have to do is proofread your work, make corrections, and prepare a clean final copy.

Writing a Title

Try to think of a good title for your research paper. Like an introduction, a title should catch your reader's interest and tell what the essay will be about.

You might want to try a two-part title with a colon, such as:

A Founding Father's Curiosity: Thomas Jefferson as Inventor

Hurricanes: Nature's Wildest Winds

Louisa May Alcott: The Woman Behind *Little Women*

Try writing two or three possible titles here. Which one works best? Write that one at the top of your draft.

_____

_____

_____

_____

_____

_____

A Final Check

Before you make your final copy, look once more at the revised draft of your research paper. This time, look at the details. Use this checklist:

- ☐ Are all the words spelled correctly?
- ☐ Does each sentence begin with a capital letter?
- ☐ Do names of people and places begin with a capital letter?
- ☐ Does each sentence end with the correct punctuation mark?
- ☐ Did I put quotations in quotation marks?
- ☐ Are all entries in my bibliography in the proper form?

When you have made all the corrections to your paper, make a clean copy. Write or type very carefully so that you don't introduce any new mistakes. Make sure to put the title of the paper at the top of the first page, along with your name and the date.

Share your finished report with family and friends.

WRITING A SHORT STORY

PREWRITING: Plot, Characters, and Setting

You have read many works of fiction. When reading various stories, you have thought about the elements of fiction, such as plot, characters, and setting.

See if you can match each term below with the correct definition.

_____ 1. plot   *a.* where and when a story happens

_____ 2. characters   *b.* the people in a story

_____ 3. setting   *c.* the events that take place in a story

You need to think about those same elements when you write fiction of your own. This unit offers you the chance to write your own story. Let's begin by reading a story written by a student named Arianna.

Sara Jane

I live down in Louisiana, where it's hot almost all year round, and the air is damp and sticky, and the moss hangs from the live oaks like thick gray strands of unwashed hair. In the summer, the only place that isn't hot enough to fry you in your clothes is down by the river—the Mississippi, that is. All us guys throw mud and dare each other to swim across the river. And all the girls watch from the bank, dipping their toes in the water and giggling about how cold it is. That is, all except one.

Sara Jane was never really one of the girls. She was always getting in trouble and starting fights—not girl fights but real fights with fists and all. She flattened Hugh Parker a couple times, and once she sent Bobby Cooper home with a black eye. Not that we ever let on, but we boys always kind of looked up to Sara Jane Freeman. We never picked fights with her. We just said we weren't going to fight a girl. But really we all knew that she could whoop us good if she wanted to.

All the girls giggled at Sara Jane behind her back. They'd point at her dirty overalls and old shirts, and laugh at her hair, which was chopped off all short. Once,

Jenny Daniels, whose hair was always perfect, made fun of Sara Jane's hair. But the next day, when Jenny was showing off her braids, Sara Jane walked up with a pair of scissors and cut them right off, just like that. Jenny cried for hours. And the girls learned real quick not to make fun of Sara Jane when she could hear them.

One hot, sticky day the boys drew straws on a dare—a dare to go and say something to Sara Jane. Didn't matter what, just had to be something.

"Okay, boys, draw," said Jeffery Taylor, the tallest kid. He held out the straws. We all took one. Wouldn't you know it? My straw was shorter than my dad's hair, and he's almost bald! Looked like it was my lucky day. I had to go face Sara Jane.

"Aw, Henry! You got the short one! You gonna do it?"

"Course he's not!"

Everyone was yelling now. Then Jeffery whistled this whistle that sounded like the express train coming through.

"Y'all pipe down! Henry, you gonna do it?"

"Course I'm gonna do it! I'm not scared of her! She's just a girl!" I tried to sound brave and scornful. Inside, I was terrified. I didn't want to end up whooped by a girl.

Swallowing hard, I got up. The shouts of the boys became a low hum of insects in the background. I focused on the live oak tree near the edge of the river where Sara Jane was sitting, and started walking.

When I got close, Sara Jane saw me coming. Her eyes narrowed. She twisted her face in a mean scowl. Then she stood up and stared down at me, a funny stare, like she didn't know whether to crush me right then and there, or first let me say a few last words. I guess she decided to let me live a while, because she relaxed suddenly and leaned back against the tree.

"You're Henry, aren't you?"

"Y...y...yes," I wheezed. She laughed out loud, a big, strong laugh. Then she looked at me again.

"I reckon you know who I am."

"Yes," I said with more confidence.

"Well, Henry," she continued, "I guess they sent you over here on a dare, since they're all so scared of me."

How did she know? I stood there gawking. She laughed again, but not as loud as the first time.

"You sure do look like an idiot! But I tell you what. I'm gonna give you a second dare. Henry Mason, I dare you to race me to the other side of the river!"

I just looked at her. "You . . . you mean . . . swimming?" I asked.

"No, dimwit! I mean walkin' on water!" Sara Jane was already nearing the bank.

I held back. But then I realized this was my chance to prove that I wasn't afraid of her.

"Okay. I'll do it," I said. Even if I didn't win, I'd still be a hero for trying.

I walked to the river's edge. A crowd of kids had gathered to see what was going on.

"Ready!" Sara Jane yelled. All my muscles got real stiff.

"Set..." I took a deep breath.

"GO!" And we were off, head first into the brown water of the Mississippi.

I moved my arms and legs like all get out to keep up with her. Sara Jane could really swim! She started pulling ahead just as my strength began to give out. She reached the other bank when I hit the middle, gasping for breath. I couldn't go any farther, so I grabbed hold of a branch sticking up out of the muddy water.

Sara Jane was yelling from one side of the river. Everybody else was yelling from the other side. I was too tired to move. Then, all of a sudden, their shouts were drowned out by another sound.

It was the shrill blast of a riverboat whistle.

I looked up to see a huge riverboat heading straight for me, the brown water foaming around its churning paddle wheels. My heart flipped in my chest. I let go of the branch and tried to swim, but I sank like a rock. I never thought I'd die by being hit by a riverboat. Then everything was dark.

When I came to, I was lying on the other side of the river wheezing and choking.

"You all right, Henry?" It was Sara Jane.

I choked up a ton of river water. "Are we on the bank?" I spluttered.

"No, dimwit, we're in Heaven," came the answer. It was definitely Sara Jane.

"What happened?" I asked, sitting up.

"Well," she said in a matter-of-fact voice, "you were stuck in the middle of the river, and there was a big riverboat chuggin' straight toward you, so I swam in and pulled you out."

"You mean . . . you saved me?"

She nodded.

"Why?"

It took a while for her to answer. "I guess I thought you were decent enough to be worth savin'."

When she said that, Sara Jane sounded shy, even a little afraid. Just like all of us.

"I guess I think you're pretty decent, too," I said.

Then she smiled—a real smile. She helped me up and swung a friendly fist at my shoulder, stopping it right before it hit. Just to show she could have whooped me. If she wanted to.

✓ Demonstrate your understanding by answering the following questions about "Sara Jane":

What is the setting?

_____

_____

Who are the main characters?

_____

_____

What happens in the plot?

_____

_____

_____

PREWRITING: Generating Ideas for Stories

Before you run a race or play a soccer game, you stretch to loosen up. Before you write your story, here are some exercises to help you stretch and loosen up your imagination.

Generating Ideas

Imagine a plot in which you spend a night alone, apart from any friends or family. First, picture where you live. If the story took place in your home, what might happen during that night on your own? Think of an exciting event that would generate an interesting story. Write your idea below.

_____

_____

You can use your imagination to move the story to different settings. Imagine something exciting that might happen if you were spending the night alone in each of the following settings. Write your ideas in the spaces provided.

• Your neighborhood 100 years ago (before electricity, running water, or cars)

_____

_____

• A spooky castle during the Middle Ages

_____

_____

As you can see, the same plot with the same character can take on new possibilities with each change of setting. Now think of another setting and imagine what might happen there:

• My setting:

_____

_____

• Possible events:

_____

_____

To add a new twist, change your age or replace yourself with a different character.

• Who is the new character?_____

• How will this change affect the story? _____

_____

_____

Now you have the beginnings of a story. On the following lines, jot down ideas that tell who is in your story and where it takes place. Don't worry if your ideas aren't completely formed—you will have plenty of time to develop them in later lessons.

_____

_____

_____

_____

_____

Problems in Stories

A short story needs a plot, and the plot usually depends on some conflict or problem that the main character faces. The story shows how the character confronts and solves the problem.

Here are some problems faced by characters in stories you might have read earlier this year:

- "The Story of Mulan": When invaders attack China, each family must send one man to join the army. What can a girl do to save her aging father?
- "The Prince and the Pauper": When a prince and a beggar get mistaken for each other, they struggle to get back to their rightful places.
- "Rip Van Winkle": A man wanders into the mountains in colonial America and falls asleep—for many years! When he wakes up, the Revolution is over, and he faces a strange, new world.

On the lines below, describe the problem Henry faces in "Sara Jane."

_____

_____

Here are some problems that could be turned into stories:

- Two boys borrow their uncle's boat and get stranded on an island.
- A girl wants to own a dog, but her brother is allergic to dogs.
- A kitchen boy wants to be a knight, but the real knights laugh at his ambitions.
- A girl finds a strange old hat, and when she puts it on, she finds that she can hear what people are thinking.
- A girl goes shopping with a friend, and sees her friend slip a bag of candy into her pocket without paying for it.

On the lines below, describe the problem that the character(s) in your story will face. You can use ideas from things that happened to you, or use your imagination.

_____

_____

_____

_____

PREWRITING: Creating Characters

When you read a good story, you see the characters in your mind. As you prepare to write your story, think about how you want your readers to see your characters.

Picturing Your Characters

Think about how you want your characters to look, sound, and act. Here is one example from "Sara Jane."

Name	Looks Like	Sounds Like	Acts Like
Sara Jane	wears dirty overalls, old shirts, hair is chopped off short	sounds tough, insults people, talks with a Southern accent	acts rough, unfriendly, mean

✓ Use the character boxes below to plan the characters for your story. List their names in the first column, and describe their appearance, voice, and actions in the remaining columns.

Name	Looks Like	Sounds Like	Acts Like

Name	Looks Like	Sounds Like	Acts Like

Creating Lifelike Characters

In most fiction—even in stories that take place "a long time ago in a galaxy far, far away"—we like to recognize characters that are like us in some way, even if the character is a princess, a knight, or an alien!

It's a challenge for any writer to create characters that seem real. But keep this fact in mind: nobody's perfect. Everyone has strengths and weaknesses. Lifelike fictional characters are a mix of bad and good traits.

For example, in "Sara Jane," Sara Jane is mean and can be a bully. But she is also brave and risks her own safety to save Henry.

Think about your main characters. What will be their strengths? What will be their weaknesses?

Name	Strengths	Weaknesses

Writing Dialogue

Here's a passage from "Sara Jane," right after Henry has drawn the short straw:

"Aw, Henry! You got the short one! You gonna do it?"

"Course he's not!"

Everyone was yelling now. Then Jeffery whistled this whistle that sounded like the express train coming through.

"Y'all pipe down! Henry, you gonna do it?"

"Course I'm gonna do it! I'm not scared of her! She's just a girl!"

In that selection, dialogue helps bring the characters to life and moves the story forward. In writing dialogue, Arianna tried to capture the speech of her characters as she imagined it. She used expressions like "gonna" and "y'all." She tried to make her characters sound like recognizable people in real life.

When you write DIALOGUE, remember these three rules:

1. Put the words each speaker says within quotation marks.
2. Punctuation marks such as commas and periods almost always go inside the quotation marks.
3. Begin a new paragraph each time a different person starts to speak.

Practice writing a few lines of dialogue for the following scene.

Ed sat fretting at home, going over the audition in his mind. He had tried to read his lines loud and clear and with emotion, but the director had just stared at him, her face a blank mask.

"It was my voice," he thought to himself. "I wasn't loud enough. I wasn't funny. The director didn't laugh."

He rubbed his hands together nervously and stared at the phone. The director had said she would call with her casting decisions by five o'clock. And it was already five minutes till five.

"Oh well, I really didn't want to be in this play anyway," Ed thought. With a sigh, he stood up and walked slowly toward the stairs.

Suddenly, the phone rang.

_____

_____

_____

_____

_____

_____

_____

PREWRITING: Planning the Plot

The PLOT is what happens in the story. A typical plot begins by introducing the characters and describing the problem that faces them. Through the middle of the story, the characters try to solve the problem, and by the end, they usually solve it.

A Plot Line

You can use a plot line to help plan and organize the action for your story. A plot line looks like this:

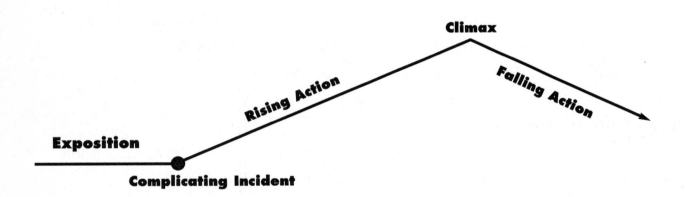

Let's see how the plot line applies to the major events in "Sara Jane."

- Exposition: Many stories begin with an exposition, a short part without much action. In this part, the reader meets the main characters and discovers the setting. The exposition sets the scene for the action that will follow. In "Sara Jane," the first three paragraphs are the exposition. In them, we meet the narrator and learn about Sara Jane.

- In many stories, an important early event gets the action going. This early event is called the complicating incident. In "Sara Jane," the complicating incident occurs when the boys draw straws, and Henry gets the short straw.

- In the rising action of the story, a series of events takes place in which the main character confronts the problem. Often, things go from bad to worse. In "Sara Jane," the rising action includes the following incidents:
  - Henry approaches Sara Jane to talk to her.
  - Sara Jane dares Henry to swim across the river.
  - Henry decides to accept the dare.
  - Sara Jane swims across easily, but Henry gets exhausted and stops in the middle.
- The rising action builds to the climax, which is the most exciting point or the turning point in the story. In "Sara Jane," the climax occurs as the riverboat bears down on Henry and he loses consciousness.
- The final part of the story is called the falling action. Here, the conflict ends and the problem is solved—unless the writer decides, for a good reason, to leave the problem unsolved. In "Sara Jane," Henry and Sara Jane come to understand each other: Henry sees a new side of Sara Jane beneath the toughness, and she sees him as a "decent" person.

Planning Your Plot

Use a plot line to plan your story. In the spaces on the next page, write notes about your ideas for the major events in the plot of your story.

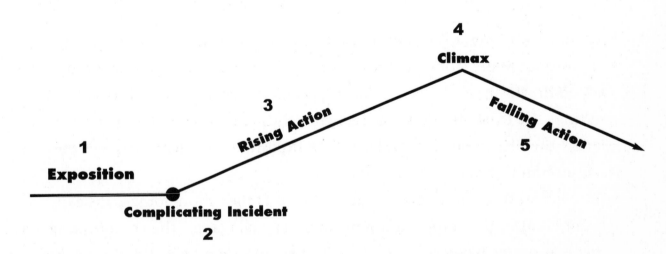

1. Exposition

_____

_____

2. Complicating Incident

_____

_____

3. Rising Action

_____

_____

_____

4. Climax

_____

_____

5. Falling Action

_____

_____

PREWRITING: Describing the Setting

You've pictured the characters and planned a plot for your story. Now it's time to focus on the setting.

> **The SETTING is where and when a story takes place.**

Imagining Details

Think back to "Sara Jane" and answer these questions:

1. Where is the story set?

_____

_____

2. When is the story set?

_____

_____

Throughout "Sara Jane," we get occasional details that help us imagine the setting, such as the hot, sticky weather, the live oak trees with moss hanging from them, and the wide, muddy river. In your own story, you should include details that help your reader imagine the setting.

Pick two of the settings from the list below. What would you expect to see, hear, and feel in each setting? Write your ideas in the spaces provided.

a scary old house

a crowded city street

an underwater cavern

a castle

a barn in the countryside

a tropical island

an old abandoned theater

a distant planet

Setting 1: _____

_____

_____

Setting 2: _____

_____

_____

Planning Your Setting

You can use a chart to help you plan the setting or settings for your story. The chart can help you see how your setting will appear in the mind of the reader. Here is a chart that Arianna used to plan the setting of "Sara Jane."

Place	Time	Sights	Sounds	Feelings, Tastes, Smells
Louisiana	summer, during days of riverboats	live oak trees, muddy riverbank, big river	kids playing, girls giggling, sounds of water, riverboat whistle	hot and humid, sticky

Fill out this chart to help you plan the setting of your story. If the setting changes in your story, list ideas for the various settings.

Place	Time	Sights	Sounds	Feelings, Tastes, Smells

DRAFTING: Writing Your First Draft

You've planned the characters, plot, and setting for your story. It's almost time to write the first draft. Before you plunge in, however, think about the point of view.

Choosing the Point of View

When you read "Sara Jane," you might have noticed that Henry tells the story. The opening words of the story are, "I live down in Louisiana...."

In fiction, when a character tells his or her own story, then we say the story is written from the *first person* point of view. In the first person, the narrator—the character who tells the story—refers to himself or herself as "I."

In many works of fiction, however, the characters do not tell their own story. These stories are written in the *third person* point of view. A story in the third person uses the pronouns "he," "she," and "they" to refer to the characters.

Here are the opening paragraphs of the story of "Robin Hood and Allin-a-Dale." This story is written in the third person.

> In the long-ago days of King Richard and King John, there were many great woods in England. The most famous of these was Sherwood Forest, where the king often went to hunt deer. In this forest there lived a band of daring men called outlaws.
>
> They had done something that was against the laws of the land, and had been forced to hide themselves in the woods to save their lives. There they spent their time in roaming about among the trees, in hunting the king's deer, and in robbing rich travelers that came their way.
>
> There were nearly a hundred of these outlaws, and their leader was a bold fellow called Robin Hood. They were dressed in suits of green, and armed with bows and arrows. Sometimes they carried long wooden lances and broadswords, which they knew how to handle well.

Think about your story. What point of view do you want to write from—first person or third person?

Ready to Write

Before you begin to write, gather and reread the work you have already done. You should have information on your characters, a setting, a problem, a plot, and a point of view.

You might have an idea of where you want to start. If so, go right ahead! If not, you can follow these steps to help get your story underway.

1. Introduce your characters. Tell what they are like, what they look like, and what they are doing. Make your reader care about who the characters are and what they will be doing next.

2. While you introduce your characters, you also can introduce the setting. Show your readers what the place looks like, sounds like, smells like, and feels like.

3. Once you have introduced the setting and characters, identify the problem. By now, your reader should be interested in the characters, so he or she will want to read on to find out how the characters will solve the problem.

4. Raise the level of excitement. In this part of the story, the action should be building. The pace of the story should pick up.

5. Bring the plot to the climax, the most exciting part.

6. Wrap up the story with falling action. Show how the characters solve the problem, and tidy up any loose ends.

☑ Write the first draft of your story. Remember to double-space to leave room for revisions.

REVISING: Improving Your Story

How can you revise your draft to make it better?

Beginnings and Endings

You know that in any piece of writing, the beginning and ending are important. Reread the beginning and ending of your story. Can you improve them?

- Does the beginning draw your reader into the story and make her want to keep reading?
- Does the ending wrap things up in a satisfying way for your reader?

Show, Don't Tell

Look back to your draft to see if there are places in which you can *show* instead of *tell*. Good writing *shows* a reader what happened. It makes the reader feel like she is seeing a movie in her mind.

Imagery

To help you show instead of tell, you can use imagery—language that appeals to the senses. For example, what senses does the writer appeal to in the first sentence from "Sara Jane"?

> I live down in Louisiana, where it's hot almost all year round, and the air is damp and sticky, and the moss hangs from the live oaks like thick gray strands of unwashed hair.

If you can help a reader imagine that he or she is smelling the pine trees, seeing the joy light up a face, hearing the buzz of the locusts, or feeling the mud squish between his toes, you can transport that reader to another place and time, and make your story come alive.

✓ Read through the draft of your story. Find two or more places to add imagery that appeals to your reader's sense of sight, sound, touch, smell, or taste.

Showing with Similes and Metaphors

Another way that you can show, not tell, is to use a *simile* or a *metaphor*.

A simile compares one thing to another thing using the words *like* or *as*: for example, "thunder like the booming of cannons," or "as quiet as a mouse." Here are two similes from "Sara Jane":

> . . . the moss hangs from the live oaks like thick gray strands of unwashed hair.
>
> Then Jeffery whistled this whistle that sounded like the express train coming through.

A metaphor makes a comparison without using the words *like* or *as*. Here is a metaphor from "Sara Jane":

> The shouts of the boys became a low hum of insects in the background.

✓ Go back to the draft of your story and add one or more similes or metaphors.

Choose a Title

If you haven't already given your story a title, think of one now. There are many ways to come up with a title. You might:

- Focus on a main character (as "Sara Jane" does)
- Focus on an event in the story
- Refer to the settings

Write two or more possible titles for your story. Circle the one you think will most interest your reader.

_____

_____

PROOFREADING AND PUBLISHING: Presenting the Finished Product

If you have made all the revisions you want to make, then you are ready for the final step—proofreading. Use the checklist below to guide you. Check off each item when you are satisfied that you've done the best job you can.

Grammar

____ There are no grammatical errors.

____ Each sentence is complete, with a subject and a verb.

____ There are no run-on sentences or fragments.

Punctuation and Capitalization

____ Every sentence ends with the correct punctuation mark.

____ Commas, apostrophes, and quotation marks are all used correctly.

____ All proper nouns are capitalized.

Spelling

____ All spelling is correct.

✓ Now you are ready to make a clean, final copy. If you want to, prepare and illustrate a cover for your story. Share your finished work with family and friends.